Fire! Fire!

Susan Gates, Rosalind Kerven
and Fiona Macdonald

Contents

OXFORD
UNIVERSITY PRESS

The Cleverest Cow in England

Susan Gates

Why is Mother shaking me awake? It must be still the middle of the night!

"Get up, Joan," I hear Mother saying. "Hurry girl! Father is sick, poor man. He cannot get out of bed. You and John must take Dolly to town today."

Dolly is our cow. She is the most precious thing we own. Every day Mother takes her to town to sell her milk. But today she must stay at home to take care of Father.

I stumble out of bed. Mother has lit the fire and the smoke makes me cough. In spite of the fire, I shiver, the cottage is cold. It is so damp, toads live in the dark corners. Mother has to sweep them outside with her broom.

"Why is Father sick?" I ask Mother. "Wasn't he wearing his hare's foot, I thought it kept sickness away?"

"Not this time, Joan my dear," sighs Mother.

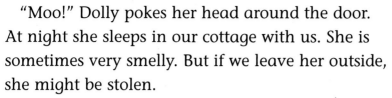

"Moo!" Dolly pokes her head around the door. At night she sleeps in our cottage with us. She is sometimes very smelly. But if we leave her outside, she might be stolen.

My brother John comes rushing in from outside. "Joan, make haste. We have miles to walk."

"I am just fetching my milking stool." I tell him to wait.

John is older than me. He likes to give me orders. However, I have been to London twice with Mother and Dolly, and he has never even left our village.

Mother gives us some bread and cheese and an onion wrapped in a cloth.

"That is for your dinner," she says.

Outside, the sky has turned
to grey and pink. I am still shivering.
But soon the sun will come up to warm us.

The road is dusty and very uneven. It is a
long, weary way to London. But we are both
very happy. I am leading Dolly by a rope. As she
walks, the bell round her neck makes a merry
tinkling sound.

"I would rather go to town," says John,
"than spend all day in the fields scaring crows!
Going to town will be a great adventure!"

"Moo!" says Dolly as if she agrees.

Dolly is a very clever cow. Sometimes I think
she understands every word we say.

4

By the time we reach town, the Sun is roasting hot. The street is full of horrible smells. "Phew!" says John, holding his nose.

There is rubbish everywhere with dogs and pigs sniffing in it.

A cart comes thundering by. "Take care, John!" I shout. He leaps one way. "That almost crushed you!"

"Look out, John!" I shout again. A bucketful of dirty water is thrown from an upstairs window. John leaps the other way.

What a squeeze it is here! The houses are so squashed together it makes the streets very narrow. Crowds push their way through. Sometimes carts get completely stuck. And what a din! It hurts my ears. Shopkeepers are crying out,

"Buy my fine, red cherries!"

"Buy my fresh fish!"

I would like some cherries. But we have no money to buy anything.

London is still frightening, even though I have been here before. "We must hold on tight to Dolly!" I tell John. "Or we will lose her."

John is staring at the fine ladies and gentlemen, dressed in velvet and silk.

"You must stop staring, John," I tell him. "Or everyone will know you are from the country."

Mother says country people must be very careful in London. There are so many rogues and pickpockets, waiting to rob them.

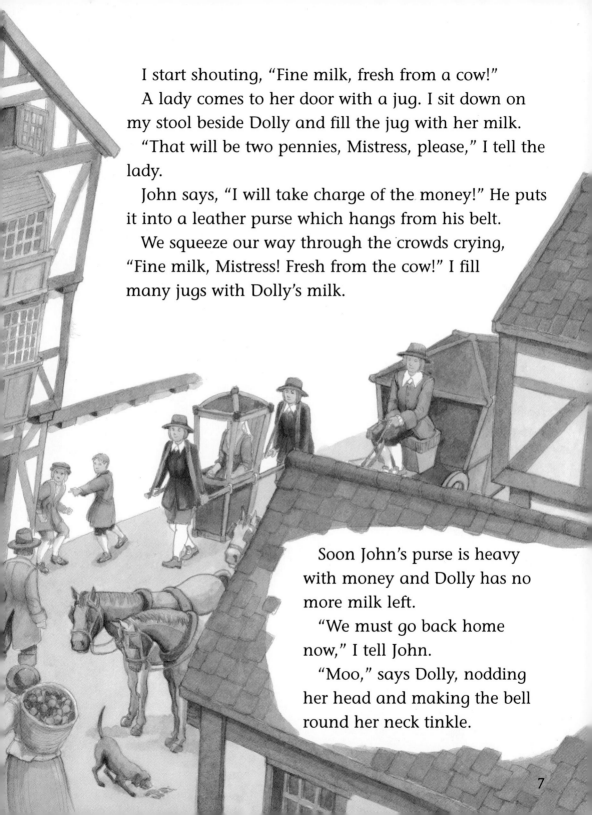

I start shouting, "Fine milk, fresh from a cow!"

A lady comes to her door with a jug. I sit down on my stool beside Dolly and fill the jug with her milk.

"That will be two pennies, Mistress, please," I tell the lady.

John says, "I will take charge of the money!" He puts it into a leather purse which hangs from his belt.

We squeeze our way through the crowds crying, "Fine milk, Mistress! Fresh from the cow!" I fill many jugs with Dolly's milk.

Soon John's purse is heavy with money and Dolly has no more milk left.

"We must go back home now," I tell John.

"Moo," says Dolly, nodding her head and making the bell round her neck tinkle.

The crowds and noise and all the
walking have made me very weary.
Besides, it is not safe to stay here with a
purse full of money.

But John says, "Wait, Joan! I am talking
to these fine young gentlemen!"

They do not look like fine young
gentlemen to me. They look like **rascals**.
Their faces are full of mischief.

"You look like a clever young
fellow," one says to John.

The other says, "And that
looks like a very clever cow!"

John looks proud. Why can't
he see they are making fun
of him?

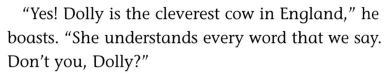

"Yes! Dolly is the cleverest cow in England," he boasts. "She understands every word that we say. Don't you, Dolly?"

"Moo," says Dolly, nodding her head.

Those rascals have stopped grinning. Suddenly they seem very interested in our Dolly.

"She should be taken to the fair," says one. "She would make a **fortune**!"

"Yes," says the other. "There are many clever animals there. There is a horse that dances. A pig that can count. But I have never seen a cow that can understand every word you say."

They are giving each other secret looks. Cunning looks that I do not like. I plead with John to come away.

Suddenly they both rush at us. They grip our arms
and spin us about! They knock us over! I fall sprawling
into the dirt. A carter shouts, "Oi! Mind out, young
Mistress!"

Dizzily, we struggle to our feet.

"John! Where is Dolly?" She is nowhere to be seen.

"Where is my purse?" says John.

They have cut it from his belt with a sharp knife.
Now, we have lost our cow and our purse! Mother
warned us to be careful. And what is Father going to
say? That money was to pay our rent!

Then I hear a sound in the distance, "Tinkle, tinkle!"
"That is Dolly's bell. Hurry John. We must find her!"

We chase after the rascals who have robbed us. But the streets are so busy and so noisy we cannot hear Dolly's bell anymore.

We have to stop. We are both panting and red-faced. "We've lost her!" puffs John.

"No, we have not! I have heard of a great fair in London. It is called Bartholomew Fair. That must be where they are taking her. Make haste, John. Shall I ask the way?"

The streets of London are wonderful. But Bartholomew Fair is even more wonderful! There are drums and trumpets and fiddles. There are jugglers and fire-eaters. And there is a lady dancing high in the air on a rope! There are cries all around us,

"Buy my fine gingerbread!"

"Buy my hot pies!"

But we are too worried about Dolly to stand and stare.

"How will we find those thieves," says John, looking forlorn, "in this great crowd?"

Then we hear a loud shouting. "You are cheats! Give me my money back!" And there is another sound too. "Tinkle, Tinkle!" It is Dolly's bell!

"There are those two rascals!" says John, pointing. Our Dolly is with them. And they are arguing with a fine lady and gentleman.

"I have asked that cow to do a curtsy," says the fine lady. "And it will not! It does not understand me at all!"

"I will beat her!" says one thief, lifting a big stick. "Then she will do it!"

"No!" cries John. He rushes forward. "Don't you dare beat our Dolly!"

He throws himself at the thief with the stick. I go running after him. I tug at the gentleman's sleeve. "They have stolen our money!" I tell him. "And our cow too."

13

"Constable! Constable!" shouts the gentleman. "Come quickly. There are thieves here!"

We have to tell our story. I am sick with worry.

Will the constable believe us? We are only poor country children. But when they search the thieves they find John's purse.

"Go home now," the constable tells us, giving John back his purse. "And take more care of your cow and your money."

We are so tired after our great adventure. But we both feel very lucky. We have Dolly back and all our money. We also saw the wonders of Bartholomew Fair. And we bought ourselves some gingerbread. It cost a whole halfpenny but it was delicious!

"Don't tell Father," says John, as we walk home, munching happily.

The Great Fire of London

Fiona Macdonald

On 2 September 1666, the city of London suffered a major disaster. It caught fire! For five terrifying days, the **blaze** raged on, until most of the city was destroyed. After the Great Fire, London was never the same again.

How the fire began

The Great Fire started in a baker's house, in a street called Pudding Lane. The baker's servant forgot to cover the kitchen fire before she went to bed. In the middle of the night, sparks from the fire set light to wood stacked nearby. Soon the whole house was in flames. The baker and his family climbed to safety out of an upstairs window, but the servant was trapped inside the house, and died.

London's Burning!

At the time of the fire, houses in London were built of wood. Their roofs were covered with thatch. Straw was scattered over floors to soak up dirt and mud. All this wood and straw burned very easily. The fire at the baker's house quickly spread to nearby buildings.

Five days of fire 1666	Sunday 2 September	Monday 3 September
	Fire begins at about one o'clock in the morning.	Fire spreads westwards. Families hurry to escape.

The fire raced on, until large parts of the city were in flames. People had to leave their homes and run for their lives. The River Thames was not far away, and some people escaped by jumping into boats or scrambling down the river bank.

The sky glowed deep red, and huge clouds of smoke swirled all around. Burning buildings made a noise like thunder. The ground was too hot to walk on, and the air was almost too hot to breathe.

Out of control

A strong east wind helped the fire spread faster. It was completely out of control. No one could put it out, even though they tried. They **hurld** buckets of water at the flames, but there was not enough water – or enough buckets.

The Great Fire burned for five whole days. On the fourth day, the **government** ordered that gunpowder be used to blow up buildings in front of the flames. This made fire-breaks – patches of land where there was nothing for the fire to burn. This helped stop the fire's progress, but it did not die down completely until the wind changed, on the fifth day.

Tuesday 4 September
Fire rages out of control. Many people panic.

Wednesday 5 September
Government blows up houses, to make fire-breaks.

Thursday 6 September
Wind stops blowing. By mid-day, fire is going out.

Dreadful damage

The Great Fire destroyed over two-thirds of London. When it finally stopped burning, it left a mess of smoky, sooty ruins. Busy streets, full of family houses, had completely disappeared. Shops and warehouses full of valuable goods were wrecked, and beautiful churches were ruined. For weeks, the burned buildings were too hot to enter. It was dangerous to go near them, in case they collapsed.

What was destroyed in the fire?

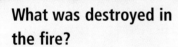

- about 13 200 houses
- 1 cathedral
- 87 churches
- 44 big meeting halls used by London's business people
- 2 very important government buildings

A map of London drawn in 1666, after the Great Fire. It shows a plan of the new streets to be built. ▶

Homeless

We do not know how many people were killed in the Great Fire, but most Londoners survived. They were thankful to be alive, but felt miserable, too. They had lost their jobs, their homes and their money, and did not know what the future might bring. Until they could find somewhere better to live, they camped in rough shelters outside the city walls. They had no blankets or warm clothes, and very little food.

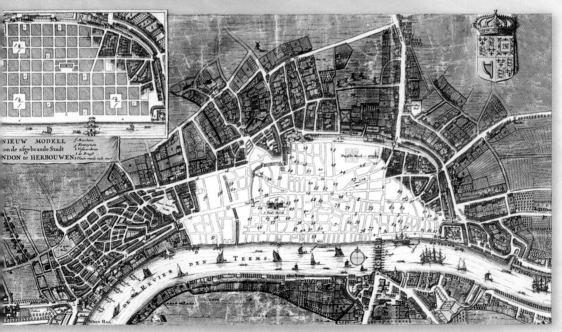

19

Eye-witnesses

We know about the Great Fire of London because two **eye-witnesses** described it in their **diaries**. Their names were Samuel Pepys and John Evelyn. Their diaries have survived for over 300 years. We can still read them today.

'I saw... poor people staying in their houses... till the very fire touched them, and then running into boats, or clambering from one pair of stairs by the waterside to another... the poor pigeons... were loth [scared] to leave their houses, but hovered about the windows and balconies, till they some of them burned their wings and fell down.'
Samuel Pepys

'All the sky was... fiery... and the light [could be] seen 40 miles round about for many nights... the noise... was like an hideous storm, and the air so hot... The clouds... of smoke were dismal... and near 50 miles in length...' John Evelyn

Rebuilding the city

The citizens of London worked hard to rebuild their city. They also made plans to stop fires happening again. The government gave orders for all new buildings in London to be made of brick or stone. They hoped these would not burn so easily. London businessmen set up teams of fire-fighters. They were trained to put out fires – but only if the citizens paid them!

Remembering the Great Fire

The Monument

No one who lived through the Great Fire could ever forget it. They wanted everyone else to remember it, as well. So they asked a famous **architect**, Christopher Wren, to build a **monument**, to remind people of the Great Fire for ever. Wren designed a tall stone column, 61.5 metres high, topped with carved stone flames. It still stands in London, close to where the Great Fire started long ago.

London's Burning

As another way of remembering, people made up poems and wrote songs about the Great Fire. One song, called *London's Burning*, is still popular today.

Samuel Pepys liked singing and playing the flute. He often met his friends in the evenings to eat, drink and make music. They sang songs rather like *London's Burning*. They called them 'catches' or 'glees'.

London's Burning

Lon-don's burn-ing, Lon-don's burn-ing, Fetch the en-gines, Fetch the en-gines, Fire! Fire! Fire! Fire! Pour on wa-ter, pour on wa-ter.

The Fire Monster

A KOREAN FOLK TALE

Rosalind Kerven

Fire and flame!
Ash and soot!
Burning heat and blinding smoke!
These were the things that the fire monster loved best.
Who was this monster? Nobody knew.
Where had it come from? No-one could say.
It suddenly just appeared in the mountains where
there was an old **volcano**. It was a huge, fierce, cursing
creature. All day long it slept inside the volcano. But
when the sun set and night fell, the monster woke up.
It climbed out and slid down the volcano sides. Then it
went stomping into the city to do its mischief.

Everywhere the monster went, it breathed out heavily:
"HAAAH!"

With every breath, flames leaped from its mouth.
Every time these flames touched something, they set it
alight:

WEEESH!

Soon the whole city was burning: fences and farm
buildings, trees, shops and houses.

"Ho ho!" laughed the monster, "this is wonderful fun!
It's like a giant firework display!"

It danced up and down amongst the flames.

Then, as its last trick, it set fire to the royal palace.

The king was inside the palace when the monster set fire to it, and he only just managed to escape. He hitched up his robes and ran through the burning streets, screaming at the top of his voice. Beside him came the queen; and close behind her came all the people of the city. There were hundreds of them, thousands of them! They were all running, running as fast as they could, to get away from the terrible fire.

As soon as all the fires were put out, the king called
his wise men to a meeting, to discuss how to get rid of
the monster.

"What we need is a Chinese dragon," said one of the
wise men.

"But how can a dragon stop the fire?" said the king.

"Don't you know?" said the wise man. "The dragons
of China look after everything to do with water. They
are especially good with rain. If we bring one here,
you can order it to make rain fall on the monster and
its fires. That will soon put an end to its wicked tricks."

"Brilliant!" said the king. "We'll try it at once."

So the king sent a messenger across the mountains into China. Very soon he came back with a huge, green dragon.

The king made a big fuss to welcome the dragon. He gave it many fine gifts of treasure and jewellery, and a lovely damp **swamp** to sleep in. He asked it to make rain, to drown the monster and its fires.

But unfortunately, the dragon turned out to be rather stupid. It was certainly good at making rain – but it didn't know when to stop. So soon all the land was flooded!

When the king complained about this, the dragon sulked and said it wanted to go home.

No one was sorry to see the dragon go. They just wished they could get rid of the fire monster as easily.

"Oh dear, oh dear," said the king, "whatever can we do?"

Another wise man had an idea.

"Why don't we dig a pond near the volcano?" he said. "Then, when the monster comes out, he'll fall in it and drown."

"Yes, what a good idea!" said the king, "let's try it."

So they dug a huge pond in the middle of the road, the same road that the monster walked down when it came out of the volcano. And sure enough, before long, the monster fell in it with a big SPLASH!

But unfortunately, it didn't drown. It quickly came crawling out of the pond. It was wet, cold and very angry.

"Grrr!" roared the monster. "That was a nasty trick!"

And it rushed off to set fire to the town again.

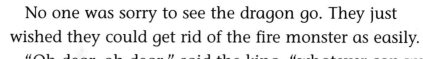

29

"Dear oh dear, this is terrible!" wailed the king.
Another wise man stepped forward.

"Your majesty," he said, "it is clear that water is not
enough to get rid of this wicked monster and his fires.
Let us try something completely different."

He whispered something secretly in the king's ear.
The king nodded thoughtfully.

Then he called all the best stone-cutters in the
land, told them the secret, and set them to work.

For many weeks the city echoed to the sound of
hammers and chisels banging loudly on stone, until,
at last, their work was finished.

They had made a huge, stone statue. It was covered in ugly stone scales, with a gaping mouth and sharp stone teeth. It looked exactly like the fire monster!

They set it up outside the fire monster's volcano and watched to see what would happen.

Very soon, the fire monster came out. When it saw the stone statue, it almost fainted with shock!

"Aaargh!" it shrieked, "what's that horrible, ugly creature? Smouldering smoke-balls, it's going to eat me!"

The monster dived straight back into the volcano. Then it burrowed down, head first, deep and dark, far, far under the ground.

After that, the cowardly fire monster never dared to trouble the king's city again.

Glossary

architect   A person who designs buildings is called an architect.

blaze   A blaze is a very bright fire.

diary   A diary is a book in which someone writes down what has happened each day.

eye-witness   An eye-witness is a person who actually saw something happen and can describe what they saw.

fortune   A fortune is a large amount of money.

government   The government is a group of people who are in charge of a country.

hurl   To hurl something means to throw it hard.

monument   A monument is a building, a column or a statue that is built to help people remember someone famous, or an important event.

rascal   A rascal is a dishonest or naughty person.

swamp   A swamp is a wet, marshy piece of ground.

volcano   A volcano is a mountain with an opening at the top. Hot, fiery lava (melted rock) and clouds of smoke pour out of a volcano when it erupts (blows up).